Lucy's Life List

A Tale for Young Birders of All Ages

Written by Sally Deems-Mogyordy

Illustrated by Christina Baal

Lucy's Life List

By Sally Deems-Mogyordy
Art by Christina Baal

ISBN: 978-1-7347603-0-9

Get the FREE companion field guide with all of Lucy's birds
and more at LucysLifeList.com

Printed in the United States of America

✳BelleFirm™

Dedication

I dedicate this book to my sister, Hallie G. Mason, who with passion and kindness, spent countless hours mentoring new birders of all ages.

And to all the young birders out there who are discovering the richness and excitement of birds and nature's countless other treasures ... you are the future; you give me hope.
- *Sally*

To all the birds that inspire, and some humans, too:
To Mama, the warmest of nests; my family, my favorite flock;
Susan, who showed me the birds; and Erin, my albatross.
- *Christina*

Preface

"Lucy's Life List" was created with a heartfelt desire to spark interest in the natural world and perhaps even inspire a new generation of naturalists. This might sound like a big assignment for a little book, but what good is a goal if it isn't lofty?

I set out on this journey with the help of three awe-inspiring characters – Lucy, Nate, and Jack – who introduced themselves and then stepped up to illustrate my love of nature in general, and birds in particular. I then enlisted tools of poetry and art to bring my dream to life. It's my wish that this tale of discovery will touch you in some positive way and maybe even encourage you to embark on a similar adventure that will last a lifetime.

Here's hoping that along the way you'll want to share your own special experiences with others.

May the story never end.

Happy reading ... and good birding!

Sally Deems-Mogyordy
September 2, 2020

As Lucy lay awake one early May morning,
a thought came to mind, quite without warning:
without all her gadgets, would she find herself bored?
Were there other fun things to aim her sights toward?

She stayed in touch with her friends 24/7,
like a lot of kids do by the time they're eleven.
Her 12th birthday next week wouldn't change anything.
She'd always love hearing her smartphone ring.

Lucy wondered what presents her parents would get her.
She'd own each new device if only they'd let her.
But they insisted that she "unplug" once in a while
to explore new things beyond her usual lifestyle.

Bright sunshine coaxed Lucy out of her bed,
while electronic visions danced in her head —
cool tunes to download, and those texts she should send —
knowing her precious free time would soon come to an end.

On Saturdays, her parents usually went shopping,
and Lucy watched Jack. Boy, he sure kept her hopping!
Eyes snapping with glee, he was eager to bug her.
"Let's do something NOW!" — he started to tug her.

In a little brother's world, "NO" isn't a word,
Lucy grumbled — when just then her eye caught a bird!
Flashing bright neon blue, it flew into a tree.
She dragged Jack out the door, all the better to see.

They stood under the oak and looked up at the branches.
Were there more birds up there? What were the chances?
In the wink of an eye, Lucy's count had reached eight.
And then suddenly, her thoughts turned to her friend, Nate.

Now there was someone who really knew birds!
Some of the "cool" kids lumped him in with the nerds.
Nate walked with his neck stretched up toward the sky,
his sights always set on those creatures that fly.

When Lucy grabbed her phone and sent Nate a text,
she could not have predicted what would come next.
He was out in his own yard, just down the block,
following an expanding, fast-moving flock.

When he got to their house, Nate found Lucy and Jack
watching birds flit around in the foliage out back.
On this day they'd discovered a yearly sensation
that all birders live for — it's called spring migration.

That's when millions of birds fly a very long way,
often hundreds of miles in only one day.
From faraway winter homes in warm southern places,
they must return north — so they're off to the races!

It's important to mention that the journey's not easy.
Birds fly in all kinds of weather — not just calm and breezy.
When conditions turn harsh, oftentimes they can't take it;
and, sadly, there are some birds that simply don't make it.

But many arrive safely and then settle down
with a mate to raise young on their prime breeding ground,
where there are lots of choice spots to build a new nest,
plenty of good things to eat and places to rest.

Maybe some of the birds in the yards would stay,
but many would only stick around for the day.
They'd feed on bugs and berries before resuming their flight,
which for the most part takes place in the darkness of night.

Jack was as fascinated as a young boy could be
as he ran around pointing at each bush and tree.
There were so many questions he had to ask Nate,
so he rushed to catch up with him at the back gate.

Lucy could hardly believe it when she heard Jack saying
this bird-watching business was kind of like playing!
She suddenly found herself giddy with glee,
amazed by all the birds they were lucky to see...

A thrush in the brush and hummingbirds so small,
without binoculars it was hard to see them at all.
There were orioles and so many other cool birds!
Lucy found herself searching for just the right words.

Having Nate as a guide was such a big help.
He was right there each time she let out a yelp.
"What kind of bird is so eye-popping red?!"
"Scarlet Tanager. A rock star," was all that he said.

Although Nate sometimes considered himself to be shy,
he was comfortable looking his friend in the eye.
Sharing this knowledge made his confidence soar
and take flight like those birds he had come to adore.

He described different species to Lucy and Jack,
pointing out some that perched in the maple out back.
Looking through the binoculars, Lucy could see
warblers feasting on insects that buzzed round the tree.

At the side of the house on a path that was narrow,
Nate directed their attention to the White-throated Sparrow,
along with three others — White-crowned, Lincoln's, and Field —
the variety of sparrows was being revealed.

Seeing movement in the dogwood, Lucy ventured a peek.
There, in all its glory, was a Rose-breasted Grosbeak.

"What's with the word 'gross'?" she asked Nate, astounded.
He laughed and explained it wasn't quite how it sounded.

As if the trees and the bushes weren't busy enough,
Nate pointed skyward, "Here's where it gets tough.
Many birds are flying over, some preparing to land.
It's harder to ID them. Look! There's something grand!"

He spotted a lone raptor soaring gracefully up high.
Surfing the air currents was the Master of the Sky!
To see a Bald Eagle is every new birder's dream.
And on their very first day! How their faces did beam!

By now, Lucy was feeling as charged as her phone,
and she was glad she wasn't sitting someplace alone
playing her favorite online games or surfing the net.
She'd much rather be looking at an eagle's silhouette!

Just then her cell phone rang. Lucy saw it was Grace,
a very good friend she could never replace.
She told Grace what she and Jack were doing for fun.
Grace gasped and Lucy laughed, "We've only begun!"

"Are you kidding? Have you turned into a geek?"
Lucy smiled, "Actually, I think it's rather chic.
I really wish you'd try it, and then I'm sure you'd see
it's more fun than you'd ever imagine it could be!"

Grace broke out in giggles, "Okay, if you say so!
I'm at Erro's house now, so I guess I should go.
Are you coming to play some games this afternoon?
I'm sure you'll get over this birding thing soon!"

"I'll have to take a rain check, but it's so nice that you asked."
As she spoke, Lucy felt her excitement come unmasked.
"It would be so great if you'd come over when you can!
I'd love to spend time showing you how all of this began!"

Grace said she'd make plans to meet up with Lucy soon.
Then she asked, "Is there any chance we could see a loon?"
She recalled how they'd studied them in science class at school.
"Remember those pics and how we thought they were so cool?"

Lucy was quick to admit that she didn't have a clue.
She couldn't answer Grace's question since all of this was new.
With a promise to ask Nate where they could maybe find a loon,
she bid her friend goodbye, wishing her a happy afternoon.

Lucy was quite surprised that Grace would even mention
a bird she'd never actually seen had captured her attention.
This adventure might turn into something big she'd have to share.
She knew that from now on she'd take this with her everywhere!

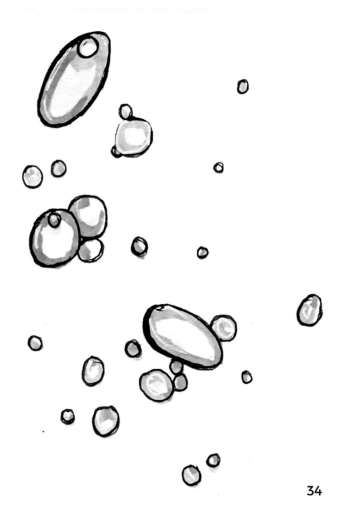

Looking up, Lucy noticed flocks of birds in flight
heading toward Lake Park, the next street down and to the right.

She texted Mom to let her know they were taking a walk
to find out what was happening further down the block.

On the way, Lucy talked about her conversation with Grace.
Nate said he could relate — he'd found himself in that same place.
Several of his own friends had asked about his "hobby"
including three on the football team — Terrence, Kai, and Bobby.

It all started when he gave a talk on falcons, owls, and hawks.
The other kids had to admit this topic really rocks.
When the class heard how fast a Peregrine Falcon can fly,
Nate could see the astonishment in each and every eye.

Falcons are considered the jets of the avian world.
When they hunt, it's a thrill to see their power unfurled.

No other bird in the sky could claim to be their match.
When Peregrines target prey, they almost always get their catch.

Over 200 miles per hour — just imagine that kind of speed!
Their lightning-fast dives take out their prey, guaranteed!

It's no wonder at the sight of one, the other birds freak out.
When Peregrines appear on the scene, lunch is what it's all about!

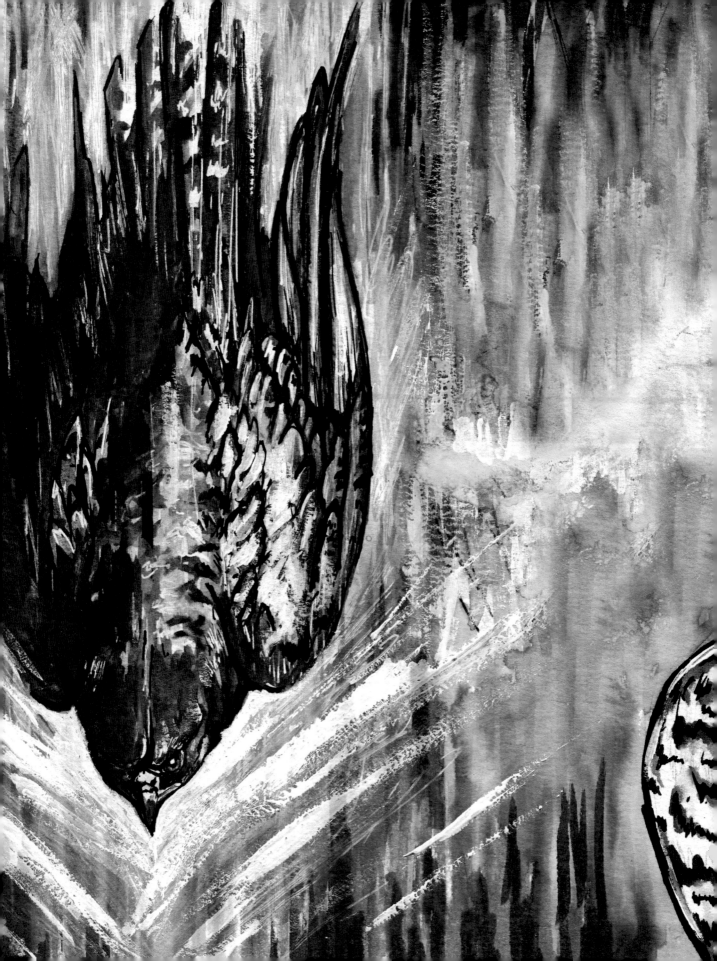

By now, Jack's eyes were ready to pop out of his head.
With dropped jaw, he'd been hanging on every word Nate said.
This birding stuff was awesome — and they'd only just begun!
His excitement got the best of him as he broke into a run.

Nate's graphic falcon story had made Lucy kind of squirm.
She'd much rather picture an American Robin with a worm.
But her growing interest in birds of prey had gone up another notch.
She was fascinated by the hunt, even if she didn't care to watch.

While they walked through the park entrance, Lucy got the sense
she'd soon be spending more time on this side of the fence.
She was grateful these places were preserved for all to share.
Conservation is one good way to show how much we care.

She knew how important it is to set aside habitat.
Wildlife needs a place to live. Who wouldn't agree with that?
Birds, butterflies, deer, and squirrels — just to mention a few —
learning more about nature was something Lucy wanted to do.

Once the three were inside the park, they headed for the lake.
On their way down to the trail, Jack got sidetracked by a snake.

But Lucy's eyes were on the skies, until she heard, "Quack! Quack!"
A group of ducks was paddling by, looking for a snack.

"Those guys always make me smile," Nate declared with a big grin.
"It's hard picking favorites, but in my opinion they ALL win.

"Ducks and geese, grebes and loons, swans and scoters, too —
I like every kind of bird out there that swims into my view."

Then Nate directed Lucy's attention to the lake's far edges —
soggy places some birds love — with cattails, reeds, and sedges.

"That's where you'll find wading birds, like the Great Blue Heron.
Teeming with life, marshes should never be considered barren."

Another important habitat can be found along the shore.
Those mudflats and shallows host sandpipers and much more.
There are many kinds of shorebirds — too numerous to mention —
impressive birds that offer a whole different dimension.

Just then came a raucous call unlike anything else they'd heard.
Lucy looked up in time to see a big-headed, blue, stocky bird.

Flying — fish in mouth — it claimed a branch in a cottonwood tree.
Her impression was this new bird was as cute as could be!

If ever a bird had a bad hair day, this would be the one!
The Belted Kingfisher's ruffled look was obvious in the sun.

Lucy found herself experiencing a brand new sense of wonder,
due to the magic spell all these birds had put her under.

The sun was creeping across the sky as the afternoon grew late.
When it was time to start heading back, Lucy turned to Nate.
"Do you have other friends who are interested in birds?"
"Funny you should ask," he grinned, "I know a lot of nerds!

"I've been a member of the Young Birders Club for over a year.
It's an organization I think you'd like. It doesn't take much gear.
Binoculars and field guides are enough to get you started.
After that, you'll be surprised — it's not for the fainthearted!"

They started walking home, alert to whatever might appear.
It's not just about the things you see, but also what you hear:
a Downy Woodpecker tapping, or a Screech-Owl's eerie call —
there's so much to see and hear, it's hard to catch it all!

"I'm sad this great day has to end," Lucy revealed with a sigh.
Today, she'd observed the world with a fresher, sharper eye.

As the sun slowly slipped away, once more she strained to see
distant birds — fading into twilight — still flitting from tree to tree.

Right then Jack pointed, "Hey, look! Mom and Dad are pulling in!"
All three kids raced to the car to share where they had been.

"Mom! Guess what?" Lucy laughed, giving her a hug.
"Jack and I had a blast, and we were totally unplugged!"

They all smiled as Jack nodded in his boyish, wacky way.
"I know what I want for my birthday!" Lucy said without delay.

"Binoculars and field guides," she proclaimed with elation.
"Plus my own membership to a young birders association."

Nate noticed the time on his phone and knew he'd best be on his way.
Suddenly, Lucy recalled something he'd said earlier that day —
how some people keep track of birds — they call it their life list.
Was it all about the birds they see, or about the ones they've missed?

"Your life list," Lucy asked him, "What exactly does that mean?"
Nate explained it was a tally of all the birds he'd seen.
One day when he was only eight, he saw a Mourning Dove.
Right then, he knew watching birds was something he would love.

"It's a special treat when we add a bird to our life list.
Getting a 'lifer' is something that we simply can't resist.
Oftentimes, we'll stop and do some kind of happy dance
when we spot a brand new bird, by design or happenstance."

"Some people go to distant lands to pursue their obsession.
Many consider their bird list a precious personal possession.

"Someday I will travel, too, but right now I'm totally okay
with the birds found right here at home, like the ones we saw today."

Now, Lucy has her own life list she started that fine day.
An Indigo Bunting lit the spark that sent her on her way.

On this path of discovery, with the love she feels for birds,
Lucy's embarked on an adventure too wonderful for words!

_____'s Life List

Get the free companion field guide
with all of Lucy's birds and more
at LucysLifeList.com

List of Birds in this Book

Acknowledgments

With special thanks to:

Siobhan Carroll Abato
Carolann Baal
Devon Joy Daugherty
Virginia Douglas
Erin Lehnert
Paula Lozano
Jessica Melfi
Denny Mogyordy
Crystal Pirri
Mayra Porrata
Karen Zach

...and to countless others who have supported and inspired us throughout the creative process. THANK YOU!

About the Author

Sally Deems-Mogyordy has been writing professionally for over 30 years. Her work has won recognition through the National Calendar Awards as well as the Louie Awards, which honor originality and creativity in the greeting card industry. She has had several poems published, and her children's book "Pretty Betty Butterfly" will soon be followed by a sequel. Sally is passionate about the natural world and is committed to helping others make a personal connection with nature through her writing. She lives in NE Ohio on the shore of Lake Erie, which provides a never-ending source of inspiration. To read Sally's musings about nature and life, please visit her website at DelightedByNature.com.

About the Artist

Christina Baal is a wandering bird artist whose life dream is to meet and paint 10,000 different species of birds. After graduating from Bard College in the Hudson Valley with a BA in Studio Art, she has pursued this dream by traveling across the country and around the world searching for birds and adventures. Her quest has taken her to the Galápagos, Costa Rica, Ecuador, Japan, and every region of the continental United States. She also loves going to bird festivals to exhibit artwork and meet amazing bird-loving people. (Case-in-point, Christina and Sally met at The Biggest Week in American Birding in Ohio.) Christina's artwork is driven by a passion for birds, wildlife, and the relationship between people and their environments. She loves teaching environmental education and nature art to people of all ages. Her favorite birds are Yellow Warblers, Turkey Vultures, and California Condors. You can see more of her artwork and follow the adventure at DrawingTenThousandBirds.com